WITH JES

I Give

Copyrights

This book belongs to:

....

....

Today is Christmas! Noah runs to the Christmas tree to see what gifts he has received.

Noah says: "Oh cool!
The red truck I really wanted!
A brand-new soccer ball!
An electric train!"
Noah unpacks all the gifts
he has received and happily
starts playing with them
in the living room.

As Noah is playing, through the window, he notices a small boy playing in the snow. The little boy looks sad. "Daddy, why is this little boy sad?" asks Noah.

"That is our new neighbor,"
Daddy answers.
"His family and him just moved
in. Unfortunately, his parents
were not able to buy him
gifts this year."

His father then tells him that receiving gifts is fun, but the real meaning of Christmas is about God sending his son Jesus into this world to help us. This was the greatest gift ever given!

Noah starts thinking and says: "Daddy, I have an idea! I received so many gifts this year. What if I gave him one of my gifts? Maybe that would cheer him up?"

"What a great idea Noah! Let's go see him right now!" exclaims Daddy!

Noah and his dad quickly get dressed, they wrap Noah's new red truck, the one he really really liked and they go to their neighbor's house. Daddy tells the little boy's parents that Noah would like to give a gift to their son and they agree.

Noah goes to the little boy and gives him the little red truck wrapped up in a gift box and says, "Merry Christmas!" The little boy's eyes light up and he starts smiling.
"Wow! That is awesome! Thank you!" says the little boy. "I didn't think I was going to get anything this year!"

Later that day,
Noah tells his father,
"You know, I was having fun
this morning with my toys,
but when I gave the little boy
my red truck and I saw him
smiling, there was a warm
feeling in my heart and
it made me even happier
than before."

Daddy replies,
"When you gave that little red truck, Jesus was also happy because this is what he came to teach us and you now understand the real meaning of Christmas."

"Yes daddy! With Jesus, Christmas is fun!"

The End.

Author's note:

Thank you so much for reading this book. If you enjoyed this book, we would love it if you could leave a review or recommend it to a friend.

You can get the coloring book and the audiobook for FREE by visiting

www.gnmkids.com

Thank you for your support!

"For God so loved the world, that he gave his only begotten Son, that whosoever believeth in him should not perish, but have everlasting life."

-John 3:16 KJV

Thank you for your support!

Please checkout our other books

www.gnmkids.com

Made in the USA
Monee, IL
31 October 2022

16917369R00021